# IN MAD® WE TRUST!

## by SERGIO ARAGONÉS

**ALBERT B. FELDSTEIN, Editor**

WARNER
PAPERBACK
LIBRARY

A Warner Communications Company

**WARNER PAPERBACK LIBRARY EDITION**
First Printing: March, 1974

**Title "MAD" used with permission of its owner,
E.C. Publications, Inc.**

This Warner Paperback Library Edition is published by arrangement
with E.C. Publications, Inc.

Warner Paperback Library is a division of Warner Books, Inc.,
75 Rockefeller Plaza, New York, New York 10019.

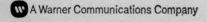 A Warner Communications Company

# A HAREBRAINED IDEA

# SUBSTITUTE TEACHING

# 1

# SHORE LEAVE

# LIBERTY OF STATUE

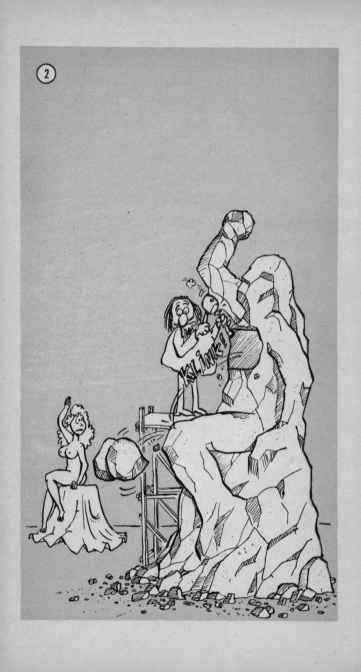

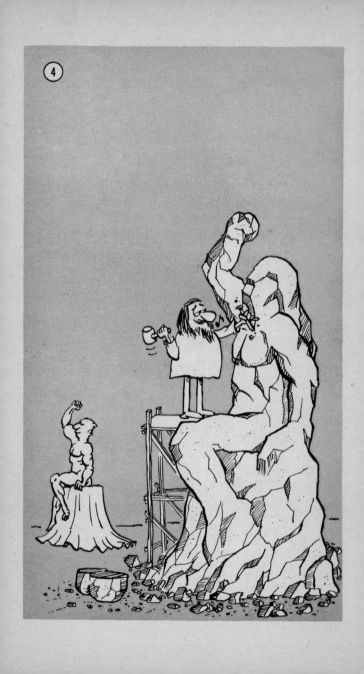

# QUICK ON THE RIGGER!

# HEX MARKS THE SPOT

2

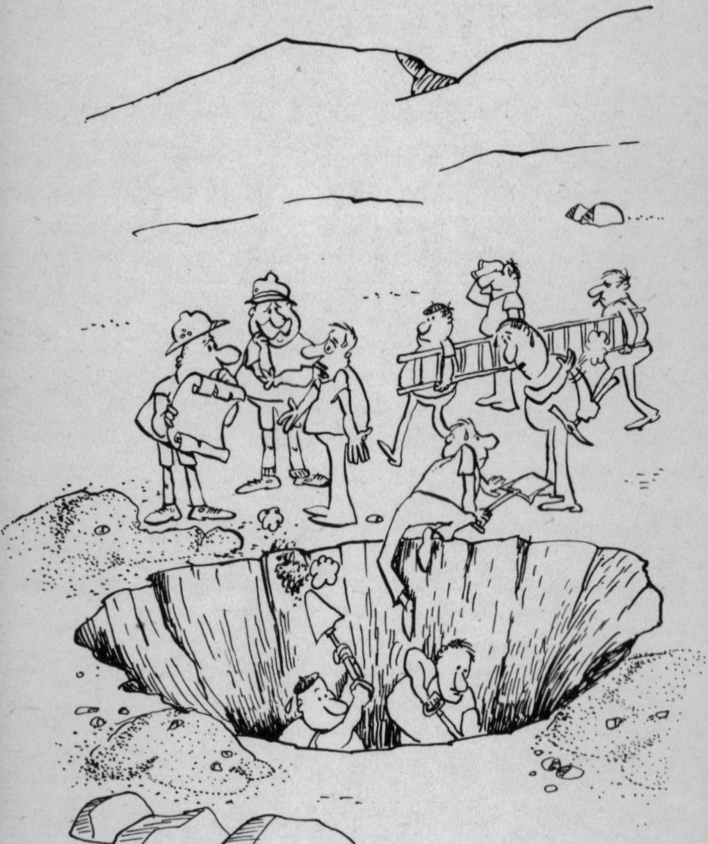

3

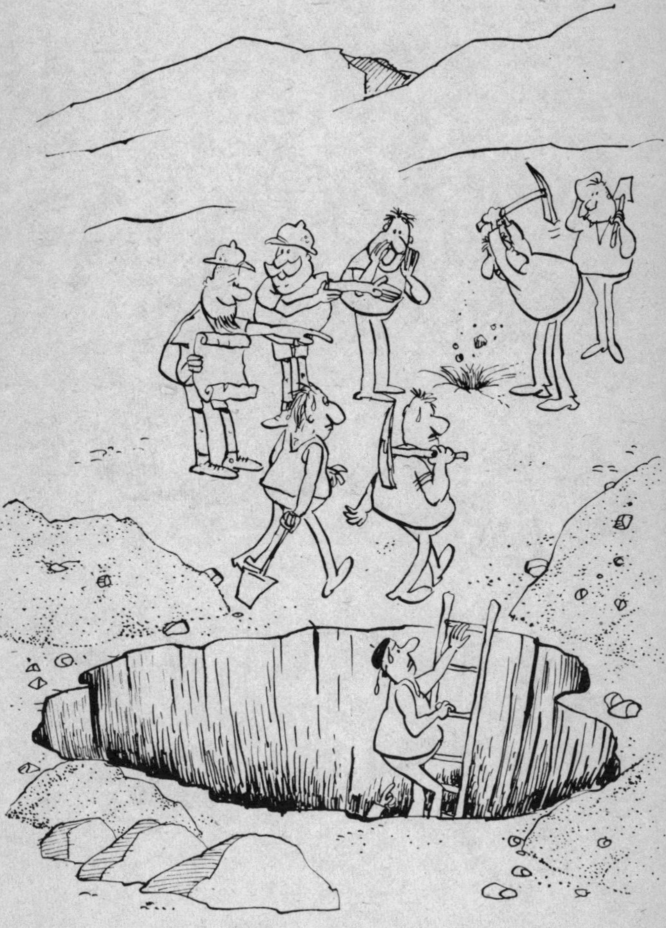

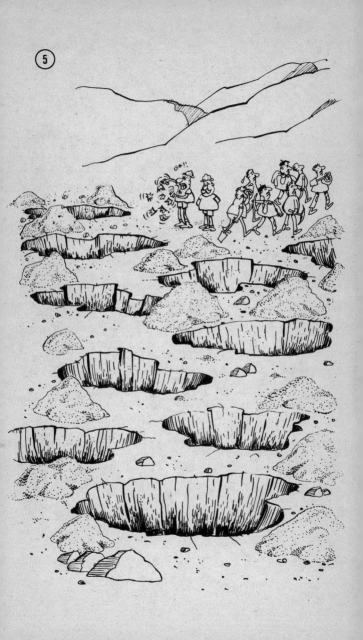

# THE TRAVELING BAG

# A BALANCED ACCOUNT

# THAT TAKES BRAINS!

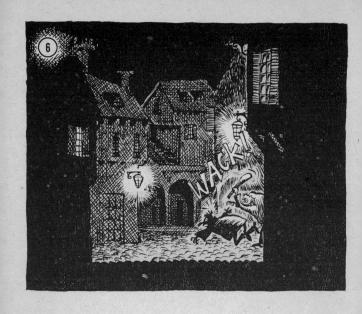

# ATTENTION, PLEASE!

①

# IN QUEST OF THE HUIZINETZAPOPIXTLAXOCHI IDOL

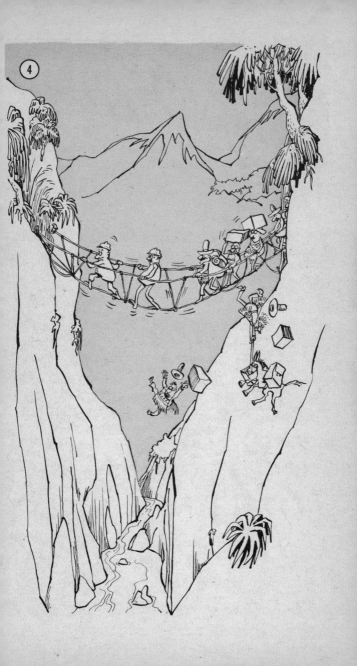

# A REVOLUTIONARY IDEA..

# THE
# RESOLUTION

①

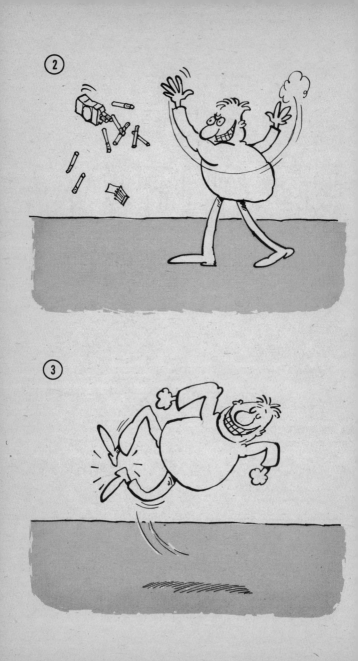

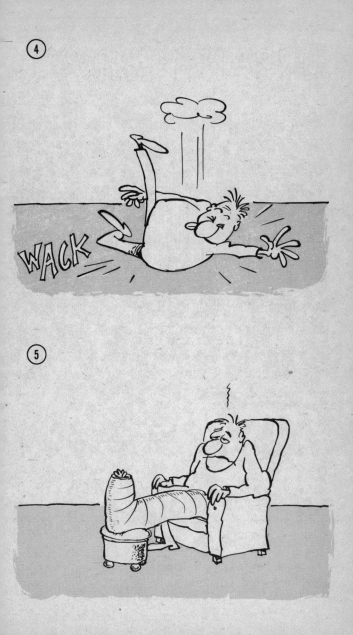

# HORSE MANEUVER

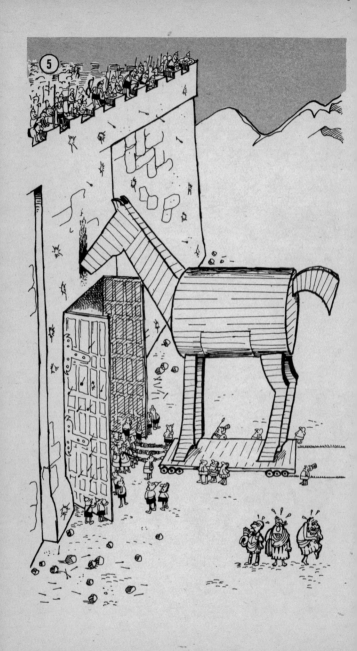

# CHILD'S PLAY

# THE LAST TANGO IN JERSEY CITY

# ORAL GRATIFICATION

# A LEADING CAUSE OF HEART FAILURE..

# GOLD-DARNED!

# A BEASTLY ACT

# THE LAW-ABIDING CITIZEN

# SNOW JOB

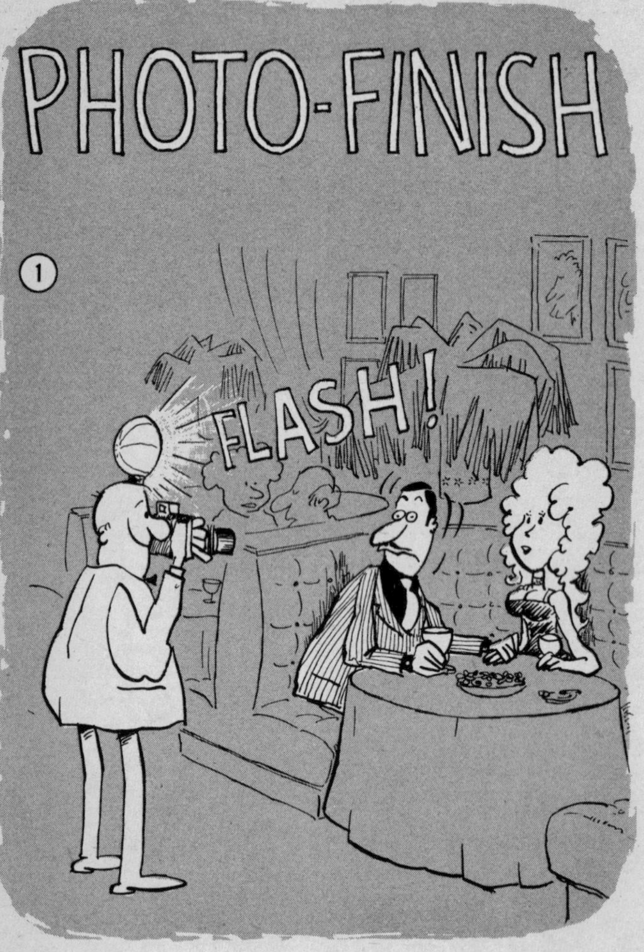
PHOTO-FINISH
1
FLASH!

# STP ALL OVER THE PLACE!

# A GRIZZLY PROPHECY

# THE CUSTOMER IS ALWAYS RIGHT!

# INDIAN GIVER

# THE BLACKBOARD BUNGLE

# MATERIAL WITNESSES

# TRAINING AID

①

# A BURNING SENSATION

# DANGER: BLASTING!

# COLLISION REVISION

THUMP!

# DIAPER SERVICE

①

# FIGURE IT OUT!

Chamber of Horrors

SHIP-MATES
1
GREENPORT
ARTS of the SEA
YE OLDE PARADISE SWEETS

in MAD
WE TRUST !

ARAGONES